Take-off!

Nelson

Big Boot took off...

and went up into the sky.

"Wow!" said Ricky.

"Look down there!"

They saw the park.

5 five

Selma saw her flat...

and her Grandma.

Billy saw his house...

and Ruff!

9 nine

Vicky and Ricky saw their shop.

up...

and

up

and

Big Boot went up

and up!